GIFTED
GAMES™

GIFTED AND TALENTED
OLSAT® TEST PREP
for children in Grade 2

Gateway Gifted Resources™
www.GatewayGifted.com

PLEASE LEAVE US
A REVIEW!

Thank you for selecting this book. We are a family-owned publishing company - a consortium of educators, book designers, illustrators, parents, and kid-testers.

We would be thrilled if you left us a quick review on the website where you purchased this book!

The Gateway Gifted Resources™ Team
www.GatewayGifted.com

TABLE OF CONTENTS

Introduction

ABOUT THIS BOOK

This book introduces reasoning exercises, problem-solving tasks, and cognitive skill-building activities to young children through kid-friendly subjects, all in a format designed to help prepare them for taking standardized, multiple-choice gifted and talented assessment tests.

Not only is this book meant to help prepare children for the OLSAT®, these critical thinking and logic-based materials may also be used as general academic support as well as for other gifted test prep.

THIS BOOK HAS 5 PARTS:

1. Introduction (p. 4-13)

- About This Book
- About Gifted Tests
- Test-Taking Tips
- The "Kids' Detective Agency"

2. Gifted Workbook (p. 14-63)

- Pages 14-63 are designed similarly to content tested in the OLSAT®'s nine test sections. (See pages 6-10 for more on these sections.)
- This workbook offers fun, child-friendly themes to engage young learners and introduce them to standardized gifted testing formats.
- These exercises are meant to be done together with no time limit. You will read the directions to your child.
- Some sections include additional explanations and tips. Be sure to read these.

The "Kids' Detective Agency"
To increase child engagement and to add an incentive to complete book exercises, a detective theme accompanies

this book. Read page 13 ("Kids' Detective Agency") together with your child. The book's characters belong to a detective agency. They want your child to help them solve "puzzles" (the exercises in the book) so that your child can join the detective agency, too! As your child completes the book, allow him/her to "check" the boxes at the bottom of the page. If your child "checks all the boxes," (s)he will "join" the Kids' Detective Agency.

We have included boxes at the bottom of every page of the book that features exercises. However, feel free to modify as you see fit the number of pages/exercises your child must complete in order to receive his/her certificate. (The certificate for you to complete with your child's name is on page 99.)

3. Practice Question Set (p. 65-86)

The Practice Question Set provides:

- an introduction for children to test-taking in a relaxed manner; parents may provide guidance if needed (without telling the answers!)
- an opportunity for children to practice focusing on a group of questions for a longer time period (something to which some children are not accustomed)
- a way for parents to identify points of strength and weakness in OLSAT® test question types

The Practice Question Set helps children develop critical thinking and test-taking skills. A "score" (a percentile rank) cannot be obtained from the Practice Question Set. (See page 7 for more on gifted test scoring.)

4. Directions and Answer Keys (p. 88-95)

(Please use a pair of scissors to cut out pages 88-95.) These pages provide answer keys for both the Workbook and the Practice Question Set.

They also include the directions to read to your child for the Practice Question Set. (To mimic actual tests, the directions are separate from the child's pages in the Practice Question Set.)

5. Afterword (end of p.95-96)

- Additional books in our series
- Free 40+ practice questions
- Your child's certificate

A NOTE ON FILLING IN "BUBBLES"

While some gifted tests require children to point to items to indicate answer choices, your child will most likely have to fill in "bubbles" (the circles) to indicate answer choices. (Check with your testing site regarding its "bubble" use.) Show your child how to fill in the bubble to indicate his/her answer choice using a pencil. If your child needs to change his/her answer, (s)he should erase the original mark and fill in the new choice.

A NOTE ON THE QUESTIONS

Because each child has different cognitive abilities, the questions in this book are at varied skill levels. The exercises may or may not require a great deal of parental guidance to complete, depending on your child's abilities and familiarity with this multiple choice question format.

You will notice that most sections of the Workbook begin with a relatively easy question. We suggest always completing at least the first question (which will most likely be an easy one) with him/her. Make sure there is not any confusion about what the question asks or with the directions.

WHAT YOU NEED

- *Gifted Games* book
- Answer Keys/Directions (pages 88-95) cut out and by your side
- Pencil and eraser for your child

ABOUT THE OLSAT®

Gifted tests, like the OLSAT®, assess a child's:

- cognitive abilities
- reasoning skills
- problem-solving aptitude

Gifted testing procedures vary by school and/or program.

- These tests may be given individually or in a group environment, by a teacher or other testing examiner.

- These tests may be used as the single determinant for admission to a selective academy or to a school's gifted/advanced studies program.
- These tests are used by some schools/programs in combination with individual IQ tests administered by psychologists or as part of a student "portfolio."
- These tests are used by some schools, together with tests like Iowa Assessments™, to measure academic achievement.
- In some instances, schools/programs may use only certain sections of the tests to screen. (See below for more information on test sections.)

Check with your testing site to determine its specific testing procedures.

Here is a general summary of the scoring process for multiple-choice standardized gifted tests.

- First, your child's raw score is established.
    - The raw score equals the number of questions your daughter/son correctly answered.
    - Points are not deducted for questions answered incorrectly.
- Next, this score is compared to other test-takers of his/her same age group using various indices to then calculate your child's percentile rank.
- If your child achieves the percentile rank of 98%, then (s)he has scored as well as or better than 98% of test-takers.
- In general, most gifted programs only accept top performers of *at least* 98% or *higher*.

Check with your school/program for its specific scoring and admissions requirements.

(Please note that a percentile rank "score" cannot be obtained from our practice material. This material has not been given to a large enough sample of test-takers to develop any kind of base score necessary for percentile rank calculations.)

OLSAT® (Otis-Lennon School Ability Test®) Level C

- The OLSAT® Level C is given to children in second grade.
- It has 60 questions.
- The test lasts 72 minutes.
- The test is in black & white format.

The OLSAT® measures a child's ability to classify objects, identify similarities/differences, figure out analogies, remember numbers/words, follow directions, determine sequences, complete patterns, and solve basic math problems. The verbal section also tests basic vocabulary as well as use of prepositions, spatial concepts, comparative terms, and ranking terms.

The OLSAT® Level C contains the nine question types below.

Picture Analogies

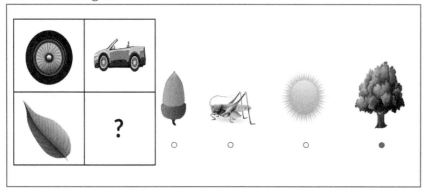

Picture Classification

Aural Reasoning

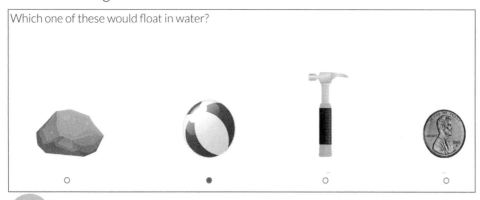

Following Directions

Which picture shows this: a star in the middle, a circle first, and a square last?

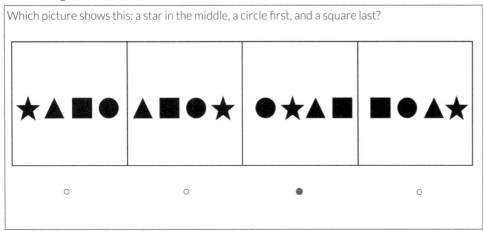

Arithmetic Reasoning

Alex had the number of lemons in the first box. Then, he gave away 1 to Max and 1 to Sophie. Which picture shows how many he had left?

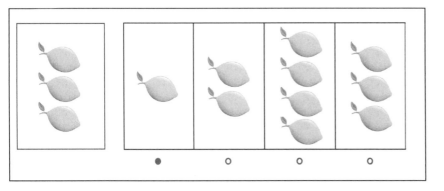

Figure Series

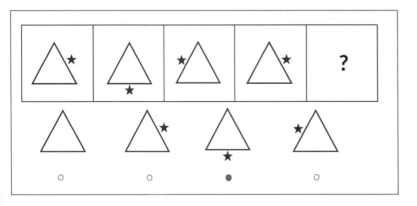

Figure Analogies

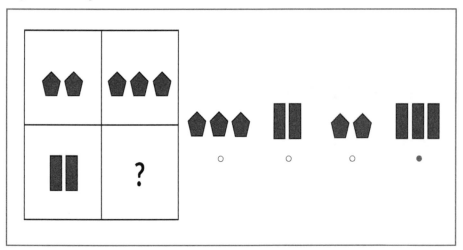

Figure Classification

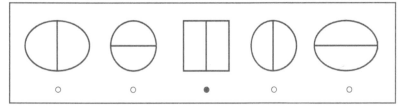

Pattern Matrices

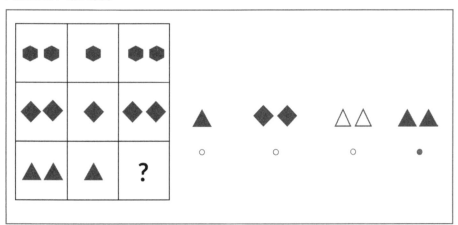

- The Workbook as well as the OLSAT® Practice Question Set (pages 65-86) are organized by question type.
- We suggest referencing question type labels listed at the top of the pages of the Workbook, and listed on pages 90-95 in the Practice Question Set Answer Key, in order to gain a better understanding of the material in each question type.
- After your child completes the Practice Question Set, you can use the Answer Key to evaluate your child's strengths/weaknesses by question type.

TEST-TAKING TIPS

Listening Skills: Have your child practice listening carefully to questions and following the directions in this book. Paying attention is important, because often test questions are not repeated by the test administrator.

Work Through The Exercise: In the Workbook section of this book, go through the exercises together by talking about them: what the exercise is asking the child to do and what makes the answer choices correct/incorrect. This will not only familiarize your child with working through exercises, it will also help him/her develop a process of elimination (getting rid of any answer choices that are incorrect).

Answer Choices: Make sure your child looks at **each** answer choice. You may wish to point to each answer choice if you notice your child not looking at each one.

continued on the next page

TEST-TAKING TIPS, CONTINUED

Guessing: For the test outlined in this book, test-takers receive points for the number of correct answers. It is advantageous to at least guess instead of leaving a question unanswered. If your child says that (s)he does not know the answer, (s)he should first eliminate any answers that are obviously not correct. Then, (s)he can guess from those remaining.

Choose ONE Answer: Remind your child to choose only ONE answer. If your child has a test with "answer bubbles," remind him/her that he/she must fill in only ONE bubble per question. If your child must instead point to an answer, remind him/her to point to only one answer per question.

Negative Words: In the Aural Reasoning and Following Directions sections, (s)he should listen carefully for "negative words" ("no", "not", "nor", "neither") and negative prefixes like "un-".

Common Sense Tips: Children are like adults when it comes to common sense exam-readiness for test day. Make sure your child:

- is familiar with the test site (If the exam will be at a location that is new to your child, go to the testing site together before test day. Simply driving by or walking by the outside of the building not only ensures you know how to reach the site; it also will give your child a sense of familiarity, come test day.)
- is well-rested
- has eaten a breakfast for sustained energy and concentration (complex carbohydrates and protein; avoid foods/drinks high in sugar)
- has a chance to use the restroom prior to the test (The administrator may not allow a break during the test.)

Try not to get overly-stressed about the gifted testing process (as difficult as that may be). It is surprising how much children can sense from adults, and children learn best through play. So, the more fun that you can make test prep (by using something like a detective theme!), the better.

THE KIDS' DETECTIVE AGENCY *(Read this with your child.)*

Alex

May

Sophie

Anya

Freddie

Max

We're the Kids' Detective Agency. We need another member, someone else to join us. We think YOU have what it takes!

Detectives in the Kids' Detective Agency figure out puzzles, solve problems, and find answers to questions.

To prove you're ready to join the Kids' Detective Agency, you'll put your skills to the test in this book. Together with your mom, dad, or other adult, you need to solve puzzles. The adult helping you will explain what to do, so listen carefully!

A good detective:

- Pays attention and listens closely
- Looks carefully at all choices before answering a question
- Keeps trying even if some questions are hard

After you finish the questions on each page, mark the box at the bottom. Like this:

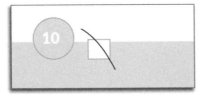
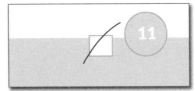

Your parent (or other adult) will tell you which pages to do. After finishing them all, you will become a member of the Kids' Detective Agency! (Remember, it's more important to answer the questions the right way than to try to finish them really fast.) After you're done, you'll get your very own Kids' Detective Agency certificate.

When you're ready to start the puzzles, write your name here: _____

SOPHIE NEEDS YOUR HELP TO FIGURE OUT WHICH PICTURE DOES NOT BELONG.

Directions: Look at this row of pictures. One of these pictures in the row does not belong. This picture is not like the others in the row. Which picture does not belong?

Example (read this to your child): Let's look at the row of pictures. We see a saw, a stapler, scissors, an ax, and a knife. Let's come up with a "rule" to describe how they are alike, except for one. Let's look at them carefully. Each of them cuts things, except for one. The stapler does not cut things. The stapler does not belong, so it is the correct answer.

Parent note: When your child finds choices that would not be the answer, (s)he should eliminate them.

If your child finds that more than one choice could be the answer, then (s)he should try to come up with a rule that is more specific.

Everyday life presents a great opportunity to improve your child's classification skills, as common themes (or, "rules") for Picture Classification include (but are not limited to) the below list. (The question number (#) provides an example.)

- function of common items (i.e., #1)
- animals: animal homes (i.e., #2), animal type (i.e., #3), animal babies
- natural habitats
- food types (fruits, vegetables, grains, etc.) (where the food is grown, i.e., on a tree, under the ground as a root, or on a vine)
- professions, community helpers
- clothing and its uses (i.e., for different weather; on what body part item is worn, i.e., items worn on feet)
- transportation (i.e., where vehicles travel, land/water/air)
- number type (i.e., even/odd)
- letter type (i.e., uppercase/lowercase; consonant/vowel)
- sports & sports objects

1.

2.

○   ○   ○   ○   ○

3.

○   ○   ○   ○   ○

4.

3   5   9   7   2

○   ○   ○   ○   ○

5.

f   q   r   L   b

○   ○   ○   ○   ○

6.

○ ○ ○ ○ ○

7.

○ ○ ○ ○ ○

8.

f   S   L   R   J

○ ○ ○ ○ ○

9.

   ○   ○   ○   ○   ○

10.

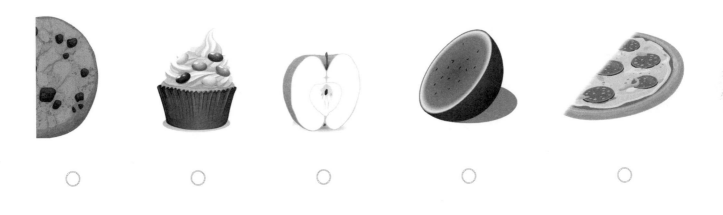

   ○   ○   ○   ○   ○

11.

   ○   ○   ○   ○   ○

12.

○　　　　○　　　　○　　　　○　　　　○

13.

○　　　　○　　　　○　　　　○　　　　○

14.

○　　　　○　　　　○　　　　○　　　　○

15.

○ ○ ○ ○ ○

16.

○ ○ ○ ○ ○

17.

○ ○ ○ ○ ○

SOPHIE NEEDS YOUR HELP AGAIN, THIS TIME WITH SHAPES.

Directions: Look at the five pictures. One of these does not belong. It is not like the others. Which picture does not belong?

Parent note: As you did with Verbal Classification questions, together, try to come up with a "rule" to describe how all the pictures, except for one, are alike. If your child finds that more than one choice could be the answer, then (s)he should try to come up with a rule that is more specific.

Common "rules" for the objects in Figure Classification include, but are not limited to the below list. (The question number (#) provides an example.)
• how shapes are divided (#1, #6, #17)   • rounded vs. angled corners (#2)
• same kind of shape in middle (#3); same kind of outer shape (#11)
• color (i.e., black/white/gray) or design (i.e., lines/dots/etc.)
For example, what color (or design) do the shapes have? Are they all like this or only certain ones? (#4, #7, #10, #18)
• position (#5)   • rotation or direction (#14)
• number of shapes (#8, #16)   • number of sides shapes have (#15)
• shape type/order among a group (#9, #13)
The Answer Key has additional brief explanations for each question.

Example (#1): Let's look at the row of pictures. We see five shapes. Let's come up with a "rule" to describe how they are alike, except for one. Let's look at them carefully. Inside the five shapes there's a line dividing the shape. Let's take a closer look at this line. In each of the shapes the line divides the shape equally. It divides the shape into two equal parts. This is the "rule". The second shape does not follow this rule. This line does not divide the star in half. So, choice B (the second shape) is the answer.

1.

○   ○   ○   ○   ○

2.

○   ○   ○   ○   ○

3.

○   ○   ○   ○   ○

4.

 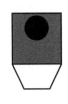

○   ○   ○   ○   ○

5.

 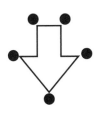  

○   ○   ○   ○   ○

6.

○   ○   ○   ○   ○

7.

○ ○ ○ ○ ○

8.

○ ○ ○ ○ ○

9.

○ ○ ○ ○ ○

10.

○ ○ ○ ○ ○

11.

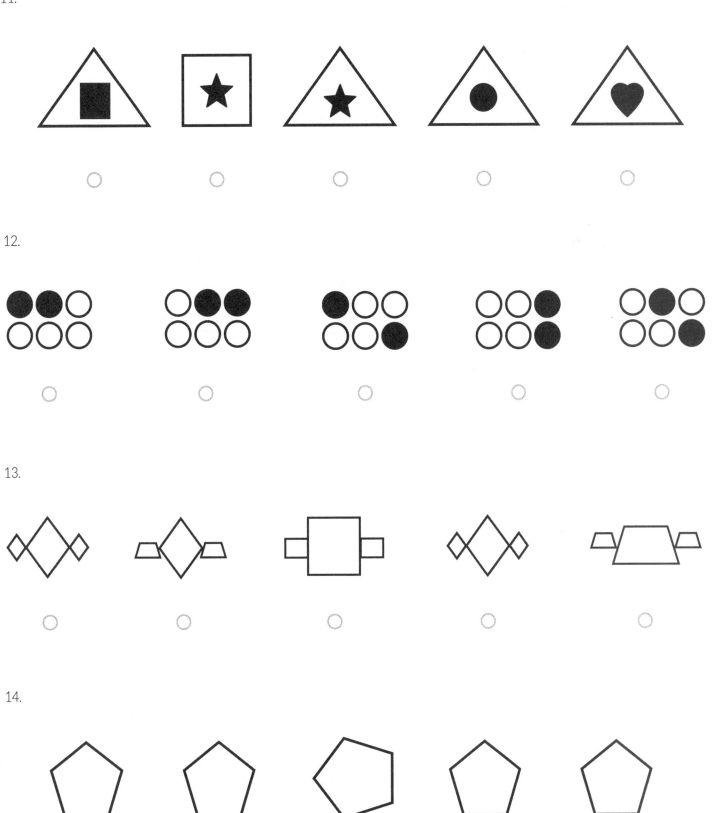

12.

13.

14.

15.

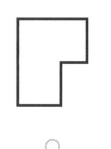    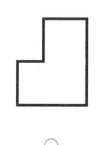

○ ○ ○ ○ ○

16.

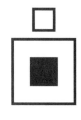   

○ ○ ○ ○ ○

17.

○ ○ ○ ○ ○

18.

  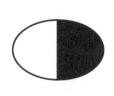 

○ ○ ○ ○ ○

19.

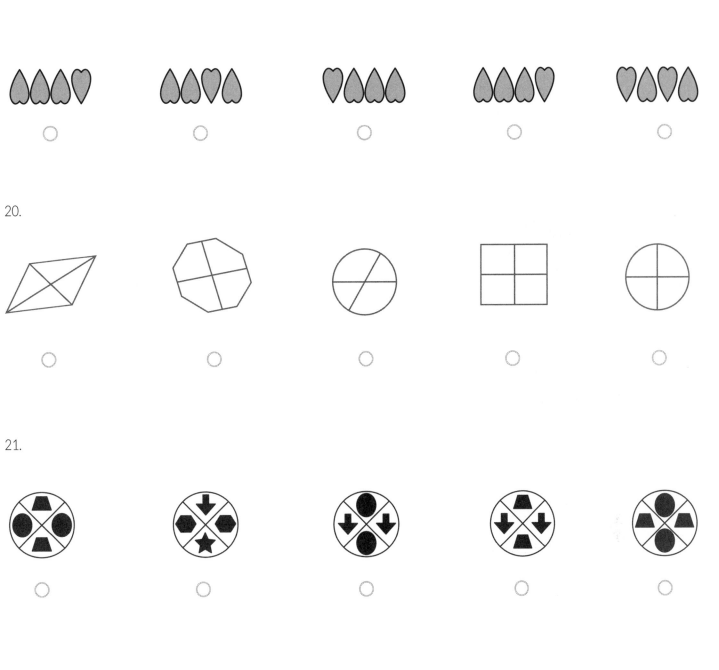

20.

21.

22.

HELP ALEX FIGURE OUT WHAT GOES IN THE EMPTY BOX!

Directions: Look at these boxes that are on top. The pictures that are inside belong together in some way.

Then, look at these boxes that are on the bottom. One of these boxes on the bottom is empty.

Look next to the boxes. There is a row of pictures. Which one would go together with this picture that is in the bottom box like these pictures that are in the top boxes?

Parent note: Analogies compare sets of items, and the way they are related can easily be missed at first. Work through these together with your child so (s)he sees how the top set is related. Together, try to come up with a "rule" to describe how the top set is related. Then, look at the picture on the bottom. Take this "rule," use it together with the picture on the bottom, and figure out which of the answer choices would follow that same rule. For answer choices that do not follow this rule, eliminate them. If your child finds that more than one choice follows this rule, then try to come up with a rule that is more specific.

Example (read this to your child): Look at the boxes on top. In the first box there is a giraffe, but it is a stuffed animal (or, a toy giraffe). In the second box there is a giraffe, but it looks like a real giraffe. (Talk about the two pictures and try to come up with a "rule.") The left box shows a toy version of the animal that is in the right box. What is in the bottom box? It is a toy bear (or, a teddy bear). Now, let's look at the answer choices. Which one goes with the picture of the toy bear in the same way that the pictures in the top row go together? (Go through answer choices and eliminate the incorrect ones first.)

The bear in the last answer choice. The teddy bear is a toy version of the last answer choice.

1.

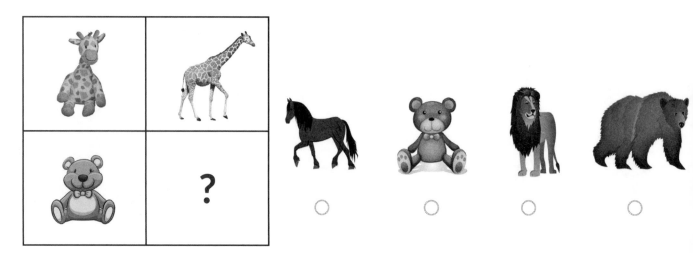

2.

3.

Once there was a dirt path

that passed by trees and rocks.

1

4.

5.

○ ○ ○ ○

6.

○ ○ ○ ○

7.

○ ○ ○ ○

8.

	?

○   ○   ○   ○

9.

I	
4	**?**

○   ○   ○   ○

10.

	?

○   ○   ○   ○

11.

○   ○   ○   ○

12.

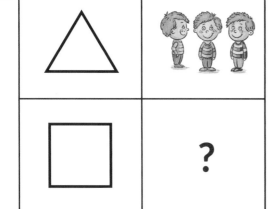

○   ○   ○   ○

13.

○   ○   ○   ○

14.

	?

○ ○ ○ ○

15.

	?

○ ○ ○ ○

16.

	**?**

○ ○ ○ ○

17.

○　　○　　○　　○

18.

3	
5	?

○　　○　　○　　○

19.

○　　○　　○　　○

LET'S HELP FREDDIE! NOW, WE'LL USE SHAPES.

Directions: Look at these boxes that are on top. The pictures that are inside belong together in some way. Then, look at these boxes that are on the bottom. One of these boxes on the bottom is empty. Look next to the boxes. There is a row of pictures. Which one would go together with this picture that is in the bottom box like these pictures that are in the top boxes?

Parent Note: Use a similar method as you did with Picture Analogies. Together, come up with a "rule" to describe how the top set is related. With Figure Analogies, often this rule will describe how the picture in the left box "changes" into the picture in the right box.

Example: The picture in the top left box shows a white hexagon and a gray star. The picture in the right box shows a white star and a gray hexagon. Let's come up with a rule to explain what has changed. The two shapes have switched position. They have also switched color. In the bottom box we see a white diamond and a gray circle. If we use our rule (the shapes switch positions and the shapes switch colors), which answer choice would follow it? Choice D. This shows a white circle and a gray diamond.

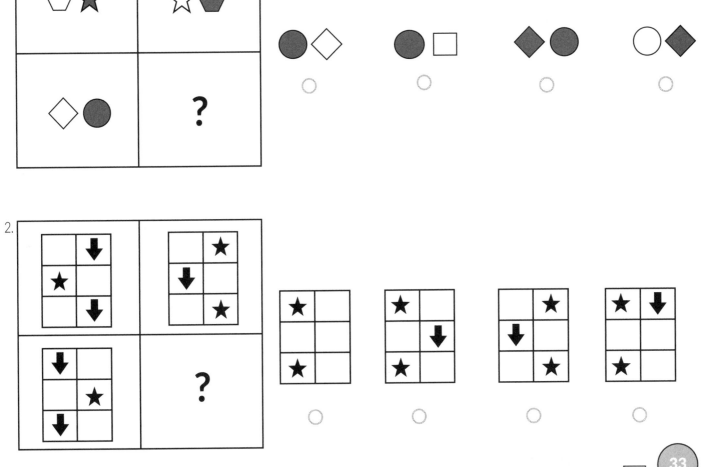

3.

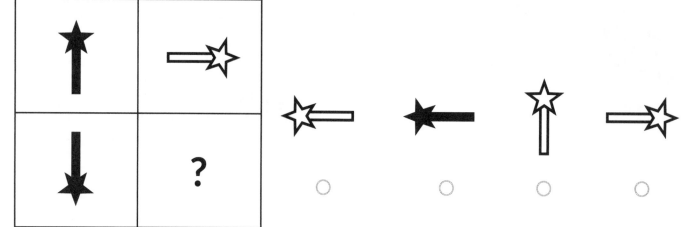

4.

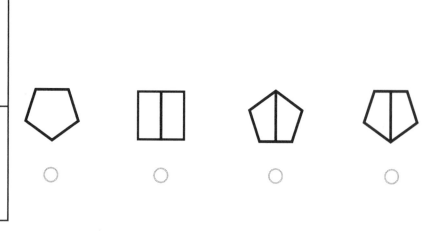

5.

6.

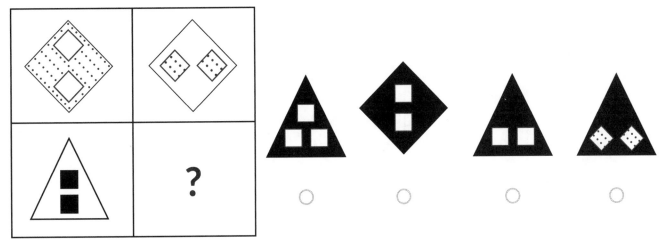

7.

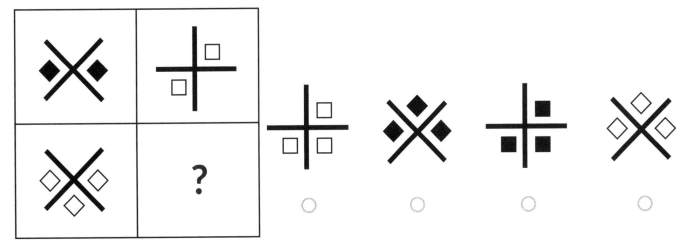

8.

9.

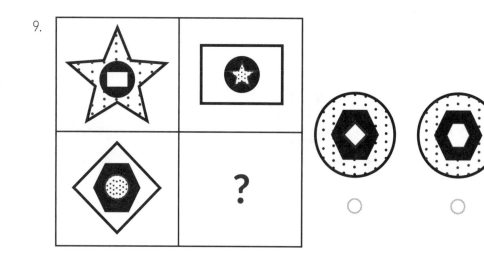

○   ○   ○   ○

10.

○   ○   ○   ○

11.

○   ○   ○   ○

12.

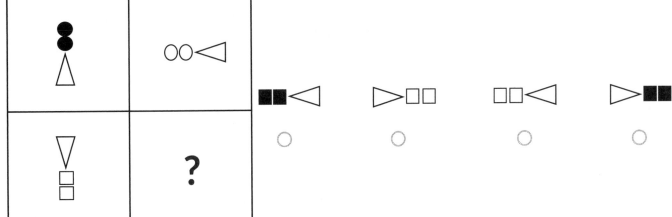

13.

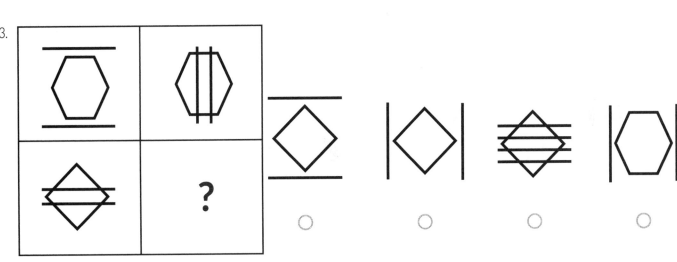

14.

15.

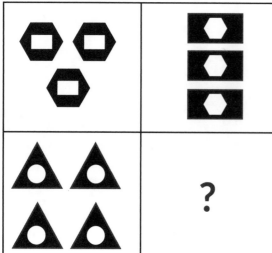

16.

17.

18.

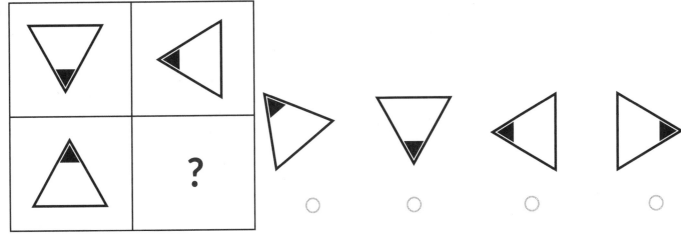

19.

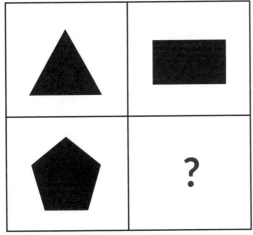

20.

LET'S HELP MAY FIGURE OUT WHAT COMES NEXT!

Directions: Look closely at these pictures that are inside the boxes. They make a pattern. Look at the last box. It is empty. Look next to the boxes. A row of pictures is next to the boxes. Which one should go inside the empty box in the bottom row?

Example (read this to your child): Look at these pictures that are in the boxes across the different rows. They make a pattern. In the top row, there is a group of two diamonds with a hexagon in the middle, then one black diamond, and then a group of two diamonds with a hexagon in the middle again. In the next row, first, there is one black diamond, then a group of two diamonds with a hexagon in the middle, then a black diamond again. In the bottom row, there is a group of two diamonds with a hexagon in the middle, then one black diamond, and ___. What would go in the last box? (Go through choices.) A group of two diamonds with a hexagon in the middle goes in the last box. This completes the pattern.

Parent note: The columns also have a pattern which your child may pick up on.

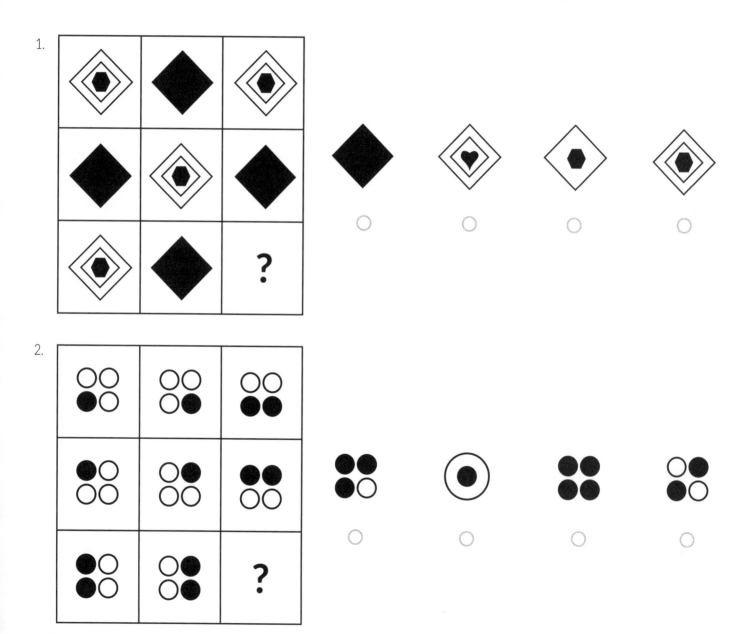

3.

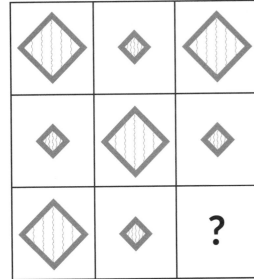

○ ○ ○ ○

4.

○ ○ ○ ○

5.

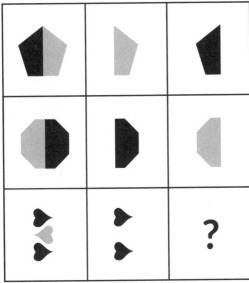

○ ○ ○ ○

6.

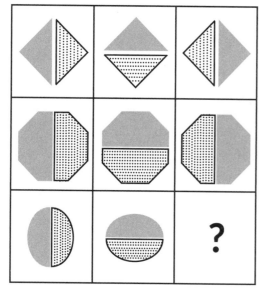

○   ○   ○   ○

7.

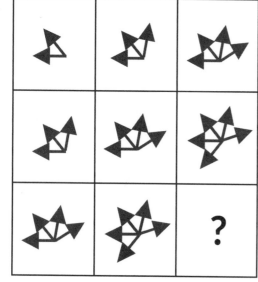

○   ○   ○   ○

8.

○   ○   ○   ○

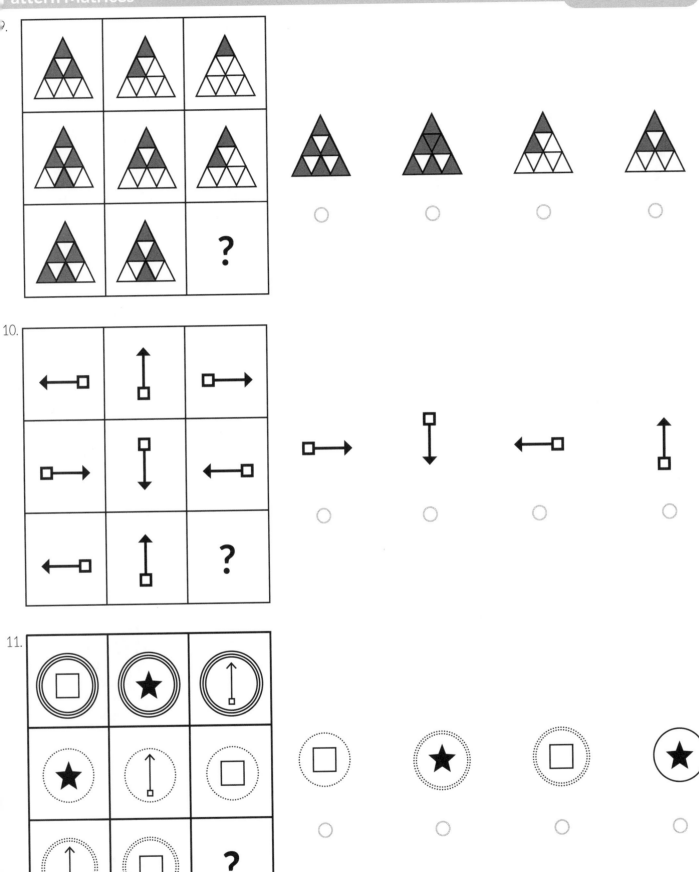

LET'S HELP MAX ANSWER THESE QUESTIONS.

Section explanation: These exercises will test your child's ability to use prepositions, comparative terms, ranking terms, quantitative terms, "negative" words, vocabulary, as well as his/her memory, listening skills, and reasoning skills. Try to read each item only <u>once</u> to your child. Also, to improve listening skills, have your child repeat back to you the questions that you ask in this section.

Parent note: When a question has two rows of answers (for example, #2), the answers go left to right across the rows. The top two choices are A and B. The bottom two choices are C and D.

1. The fruits Max used to make a fruit salad were watermelon, grapes, blueberries, strawberries, and apples. Which fruit did Max <u>not</u> use to make his fruit salad?

○   ○   ○   ○

2. Which picture that shows the flowers neither in front of the vase nor behind the vase?

○   ○

○   ○

3. Which picture shows a car beneath a square and a ball above a triangle?

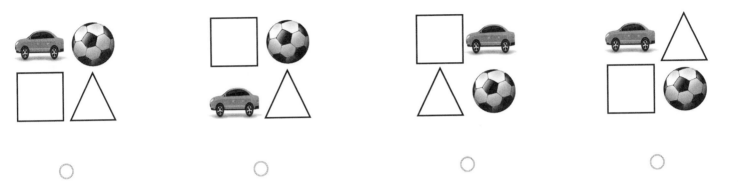

○   ○   ○   ○

4. Which picture shows a hat on top of a bag, a picture to the right of the clock, and 3 boxes to the left of the shelf?

   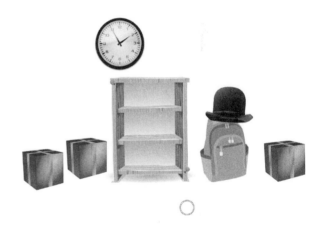

○   ○

○   ○

5. Your friend, Daniel, is a biologist. Which one of these would he use at work?

○   ○   ○   ○

6. Look at these foods. Max needs to choose the one that would contain the most seeds. Which one should he choose?

○   ○   ○   ○

7. In which one of these pictures would the water be the deepest?

○   ○   ○   ○

8. Which of these foods is produced by an animal?

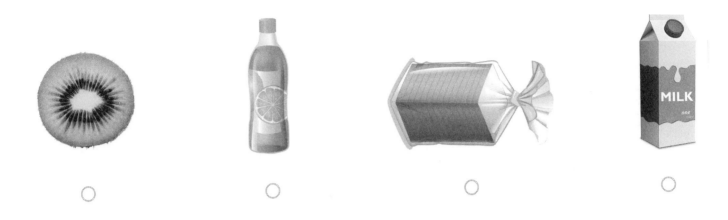

○   ○   ○   ○

9. Your friend, Katie, is an architect. Which one of these would she help create?

○   ○   ○   ○

10. Which one of these is battery-operated?

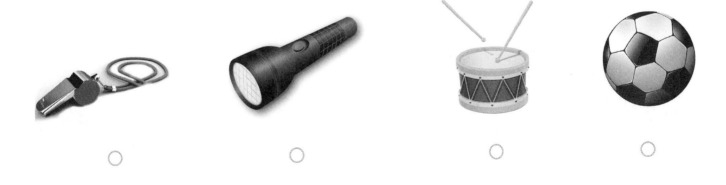

○   ○   ○   ○

11. If Max and you were looking at an atlas, which one of these would you most likely see?

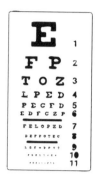 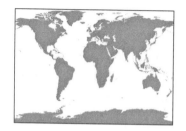  

○　　　　　　○　　　　　　○　　　　　　○

12. Which one of these symbols means parking is <u>not</u> allowed?

○　　　　　　○　　　　　　○　　　　　　○

13. Which one of these is a signal?

○　　　　　　○　　　　　　○　　　　　　○

14. Max told you that there has been a drought where he lives. Which one of these pictures would show where Max lives?

○ ○ ○ ○

15. Which one of these shows a type of currency?

○ ○ ○ ○

16. Max is going on a trip to a place with a polar climate. Which animal would Max <u>not</u> see on his trip?

○ ○ ○ ○

17. Which choice shows a heart at the end, a diamond in the middle, and does not have a rectangle?

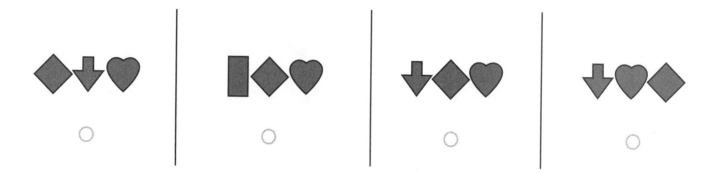

○   ○   ○   ○

18. Which choice has the letter "S" in between the letter "C" and the letter "T", where the letter "T" is to the right of the letter "S"?

FCTS | STCF | TSFC | CSTF

○   ○   ○   ○

19. Which shows a triangle in the middle, a circle at the end, and doesn't have a star?

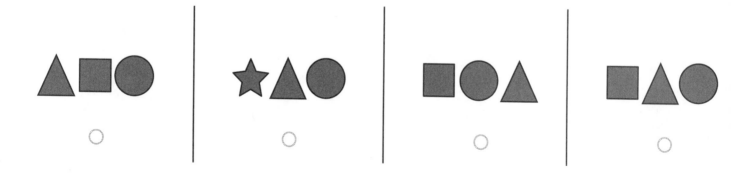

○   ○   ○   ○

20. Which shows these 3 different things: something to wear when it's hot, something to wear when it's cold, and something to use when it's rainy?

21. Which shows one animal that can both fly and swim and another animal that cannot fly, but it can swim?

22. Which shows 1 living thing and another non-living thing?

ANYA NEEDS YOUR HELP WITH PATTERNS.

Directions: Look at this row of boxes. The pictures that are inside belong together in some way. Another picture should go inside the empty box. Under the boxes is a row of pictures. Which one should go in this empty box?

Example (read this to your child): Here is a row of boxes. The pictures inside the boxes have made a pattern. In the first box there are 4 triangles - all of them point up. In the second box there are 4 triangles - 3 point up, but the last one points down. In the third box there are 4 triangles - 2 point up and the last 2 point down. In the fourth box there are 4 triangles - 1 points up and the last 3 point down. We see that in each box, 1 more triangle on the right points down. What should go in the empty box to finish the pattern? (Go through the answer choices together.) The answer choice with 4 triangles pointing down completes the pattern. The last choice, D, is correct.

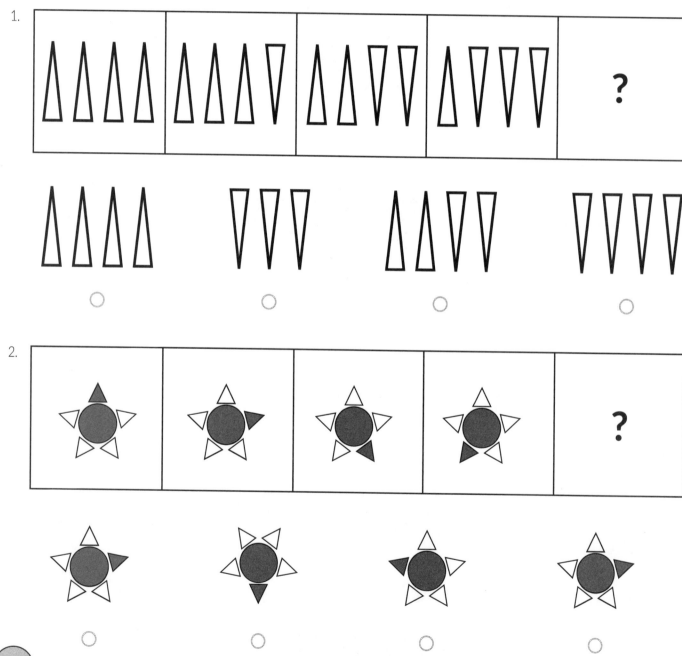

1.

2.

3.

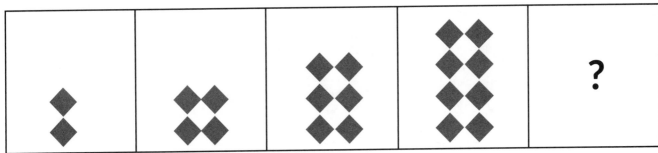

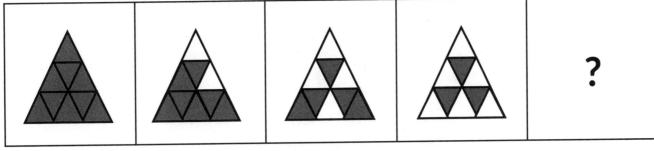

○   ○   ○   ○

4.

○   ○   ○   ○

5.

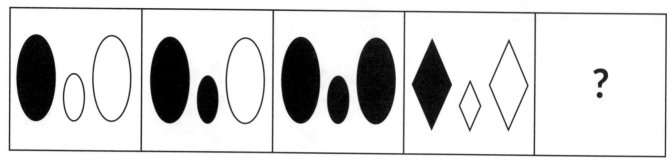

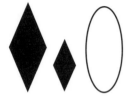 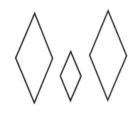 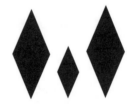

◯ ◯ ◯ ◯

6.

 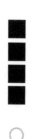  

◯ ◯ ◯ ◯

7.

				?

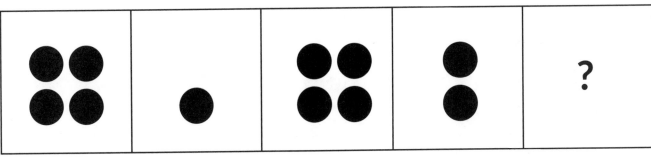

○　　　　　○　　　　　○　　　　　○

8.

				?

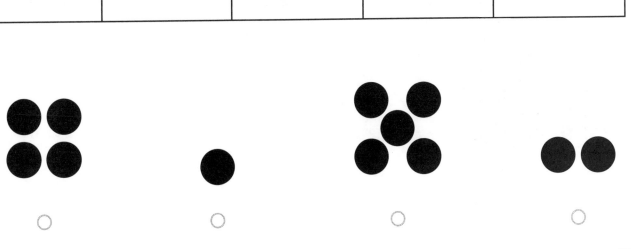

○　　　　　○　　　　　○　　　　　○

9.

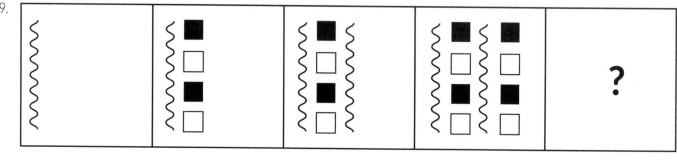

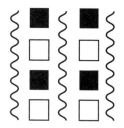   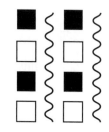   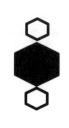   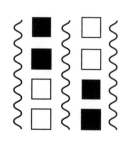   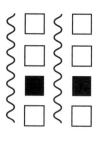

○   ○   ○   ○

10.

○   ○   ○   ○

11.

				?

○   ○   ○   ○

12.

W P E B	P E B W	E B W P	B W P E	?

W B E P   W P E B   B E P W   E P B W

○   ○   ○   ○

LET'S HELP ANYA AND ALEX AT THE TOY STORE!

Directions: Listen to the question and then choose your answer. (Parents, try to read each question only one time so your child can practice listening skills. Each question is above the corresponding set of boxes.)

1. Anya has the number of robots and dolls in the first box. Which answer choice shows how many more dolls Anya needs so that she would have more dolls than robots?

2. Alex has the number of toy cars in the first box. For each toy car that Alex has, he has triple the amount of toy trains. Which answer choice shows how many toy trains he has?

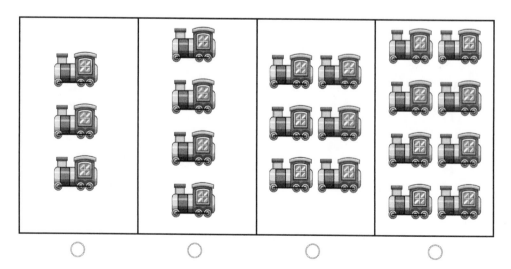

3. In the first box is a bunch of balloons that Anya, Alex, and Max found at the toy store. There are 7 balloons in the bunch. Anya took 1 balloon. Max took double the amount that Anya took. Alex took 1 less balloon than Max. Which answer choice shows how many balloons were left after everyone had taken their balloons?

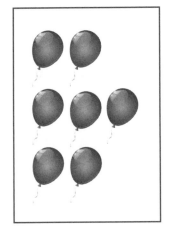
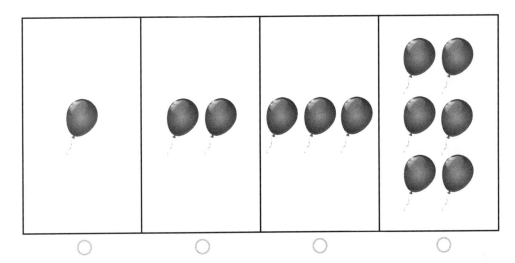

4. In the first box are the toys that Anya put in her shopping cart at the toy store. Alex also has a shopping cart. In Alex's shopping cart, he put half the number of cars that Anya put in her cart. He also put four less planes than Anya put in her cart. Which answer choice shows the toys in Alex's shopping cart?

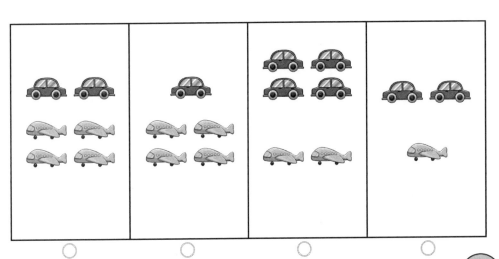

5. At the toy store, they sell dolls' socks in pairs. Anya already has the amount of socks that is in the first box. Then, she gives away three pairs to Alex. Which answer choice shows the number of socks that Anya now has, after giving away three pairs to Alex?

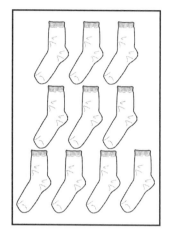

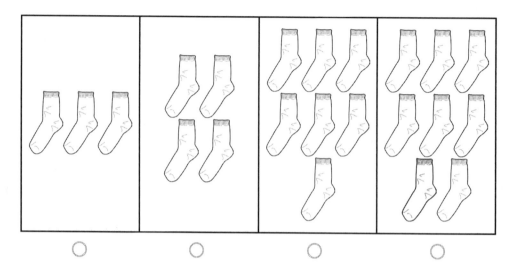

○   ○   ○   ○

6. Alex has the number of toy trucks in the first box. Anya has five times the number of toy trucks as Alex. Which answer choice shows the number of toy trucks Anya has?

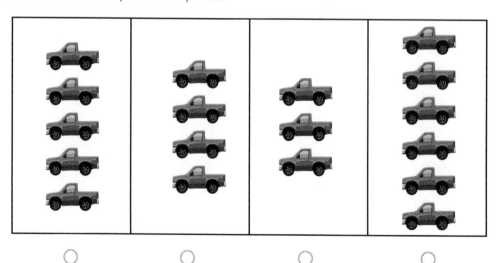

○   ○   ○   ○

7. In the first box are a dozen pencils that Anya buys at the store. If she gives away half a dozen of these pencils to her brother, how many pencils will she have left for herself?

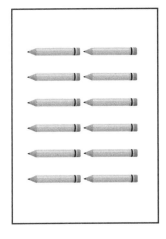
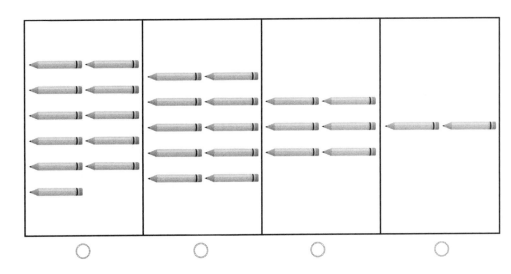

8. In the first box are a dozen pencils that Alex buys at the store. If he gives away half a dozen of these pencils to his sister and then gives away four more pencils to his brother, how many pencils will he have left for himself?

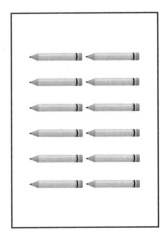
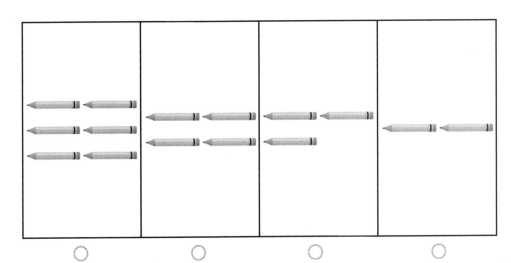

9. Anya buys the number of teddy bears in the first box. If Anya gives away two teddy bears to her sister and gives away two teddy bears to her brother, how many teddy bears will she have left for herself?

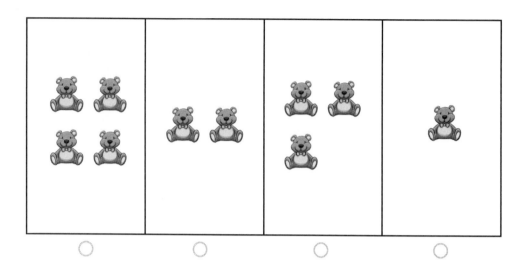

10. Alex buys the number of balloons in the first box. Then, one-quarter of the balloons pop. Which answer choice shows how many balloons are left?

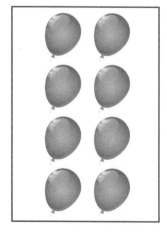
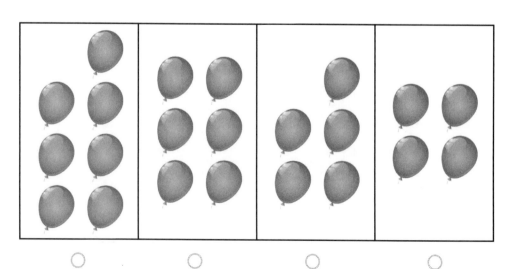

11. Anya buys the number of balloons in the first box. Then, one quarter of the balloons pop. Then, Anya gives two of the balloons that are left to Alex. Then, she gives Max the same amount as she gave Alex. Which answer choice shows how many balloons Anya has left?

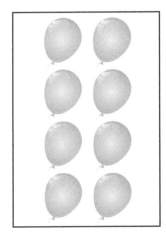 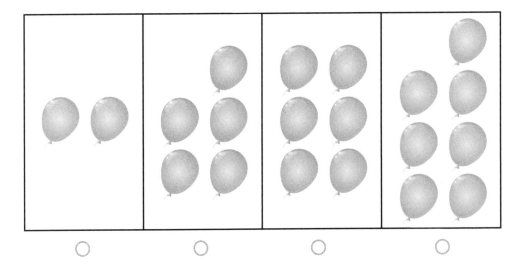

12. Alex has the number of balloons in the first box. Anya has four times as many balloons as Alex. Which answer choice shows the number of balloons Anya has?

 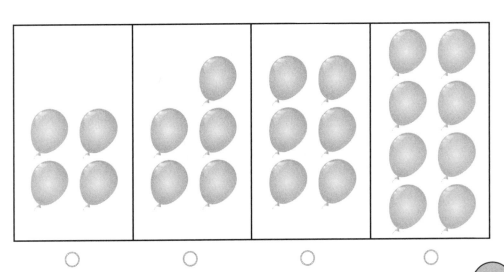

PRACTICE QUESTION SET INSTRUCTIONS

✂ Please cut out pages 88-95. (These pages are: the Answer Key for the Workbook and the Directions & Answer Key for the Practice Question Set.)

Reading Directions: Tell your child to listen carefully (like a detective!), because you can read the directions to him/her only one time. (Test administrators often read directions only once.)

Test instructors will not let your child know if his/her answers are correct/incorrect. If you wish for the Practice Question Set to serve as a "practice test," then as your child completes the Practice Question Set, we suggest you do the same. Instead of saying if answers are correct/incorrect, you could say something like, "Nice work, let's try some more."

Navigation Figures: Assuming your child has completed the Workbook, then (s)he is familiar with exercise format (navigating through pages with rows of questions). To make test navigation easier for kids, some gifted tests use image markers in place of question numbers and in place of page numbers.

We include these "markers" so that your child can be familiar with them.

When your child needs to look at a new page, you would say, for example, "Find the page where there is a train at the bottom." When your child needs to look at a question, you would say, for example, "Find the row where there is a star."

These markers are listed on the Directions & Answer Key pages so that you can read them to your child.

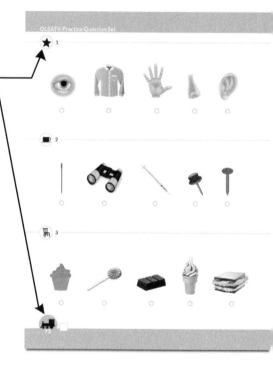

"Bubbles" and Answer Choices: The Practice Question Set has answer bubbles. (See page 6 for more on "bubbles.") Answer choices are indicated with corresponding letters in the Answer Key.

Time: Allow one minute per question, approximately.

Evaluation: The Practice Question Set is labeled by question type on the Answer Key. After your child is done, on your own (without your child) go through the Set by question type, writing the number answered correctly in the space provided on the answer key. While these practice questions are not meant to be used in place of an official assessment, these will provide a general overview of strengths/weaknesses, as they pertain to test question type. For questions your child didn't answer correctly, go over the question and answer choices again with him/her. Compare the answer choices, specifically what makes the correct answer choice the right choice. Since gifted programs typically accept only top performers, you may wish to do additional practice. **We offer a free e-book of 40+ questions. Please see page 95 for details.**

See page 90 for question prompts and for additional instructions for each test section.

OLSAT®
Practice
Question
Set

1

○ ○ ○ ○ ○

 2

3　7　9　15　26

○ ○ ○ ○ ○

 3

○ ○ ○ ○ ○

4

   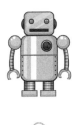

○   ○   ○   ○   ○

 5

○   ○   ○   ○   ○

 6

○   ○   ○   ○   ○

7

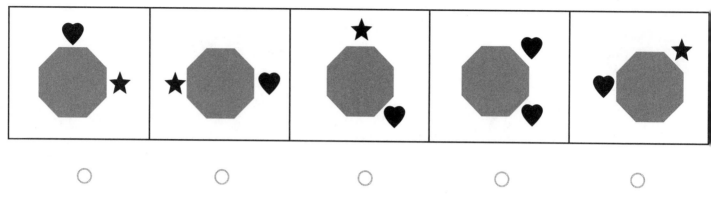

○   ○   ○   ○   ○

 8

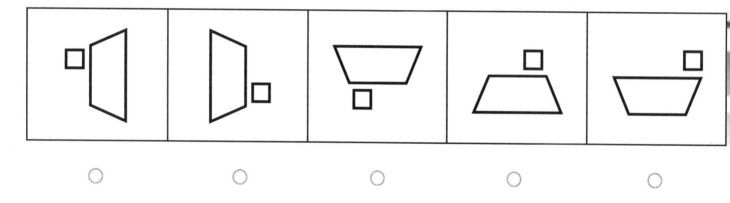

○   ○   ○   ○   ○

 9

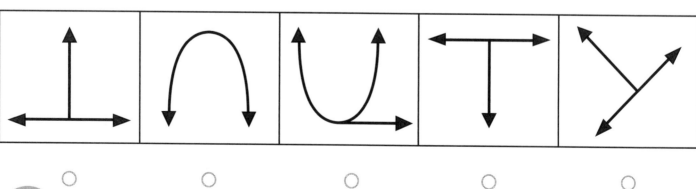

○   ○   ○   ○   ○

10

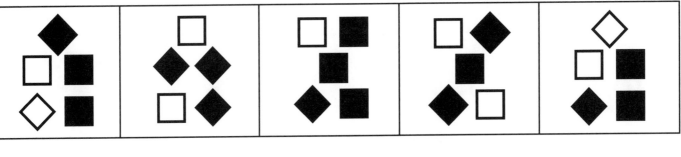

○ ○ ○ ○ ○

 11

○ ○ ○ ○

 12

   ○

13

○　　　○　　　○　　　○

 14

○　　　○　　　○　　　○

 15

○　　　○　　　○　　　○

16

○   ○   ○   ○

 17

○   ○   ○   ○

 18

○   ○   ○   ○

19

○　　　　　○　　　　　○　　　　　○

 20

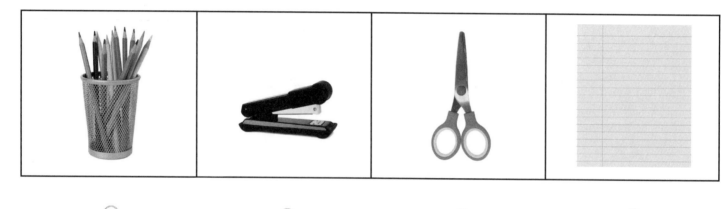

○　　　　　○　　　　　○　　　　　○

 21

○　　　　　○　　　　　○　　　　　○

22

  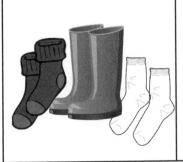

○   ○   ○   ○

 23

○   ○   ○   ○

 24

○   ○   ○   ○

25

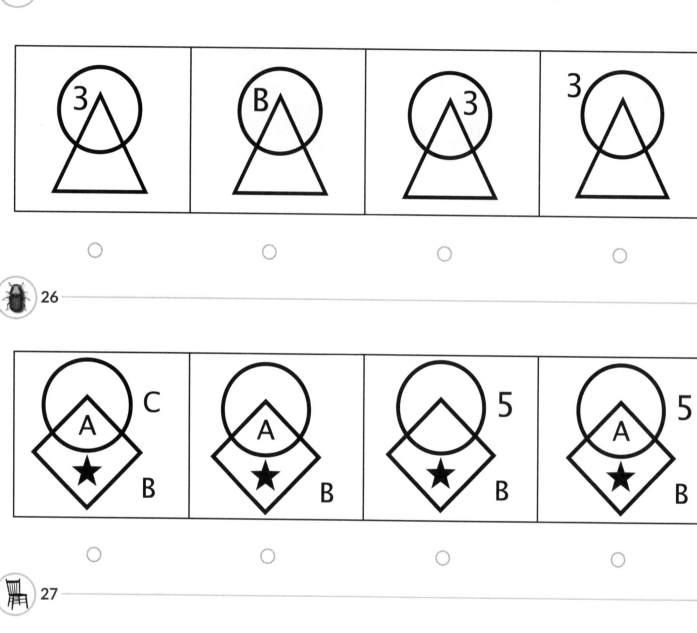

 26

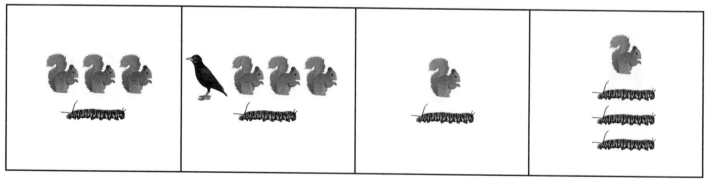

 27

28

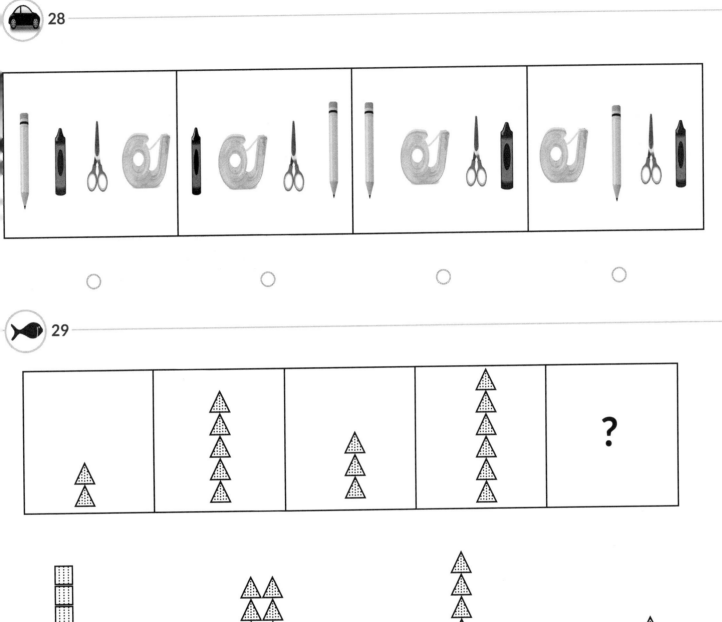

○   ○   ○   ○

29

○   ○   ○   ○

Continue to the next page.

30

○   ○   ○   ○

 31

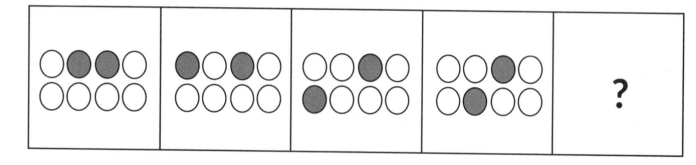

○   ○   ○   ○

32

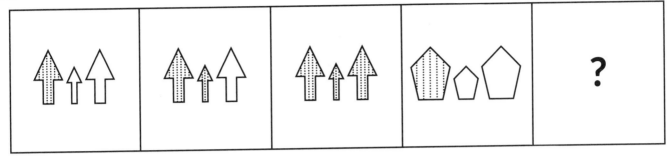

 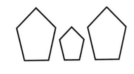 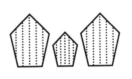 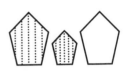

○　　　　○　　　　○　　　　○

33

○　　　　○　　　　○　　　　○

34

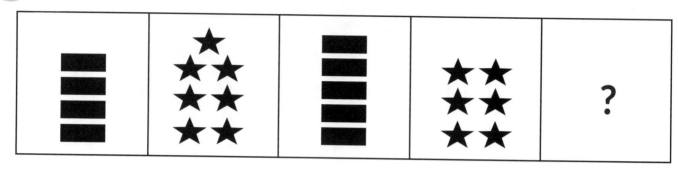

○   ○   ○   ○

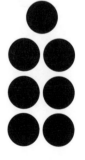 35

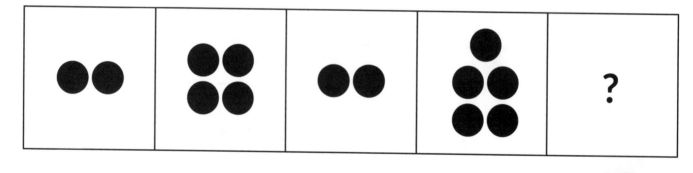

     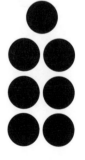

○   ○   ○   ○

36

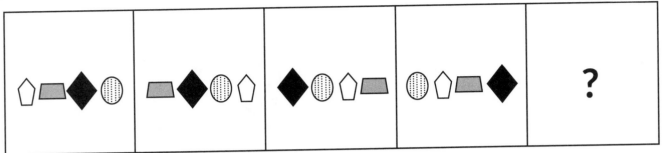

○   ○   ○   ○

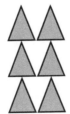 37

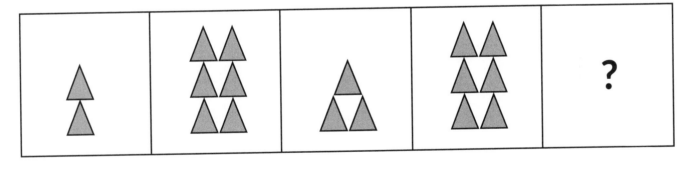

○   ○   ○   ○

38

○ ○ ○ ○

39

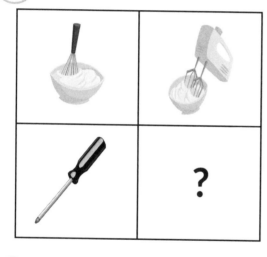

○ ○ ○ ○

40

○ ○ ○ ○

41

 42

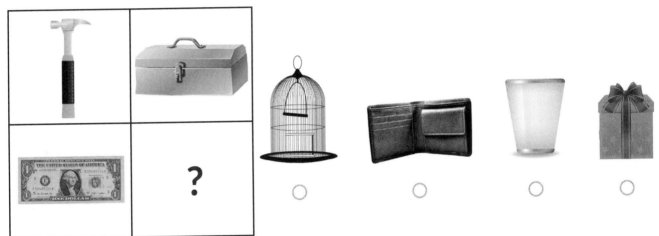

 43

81

44

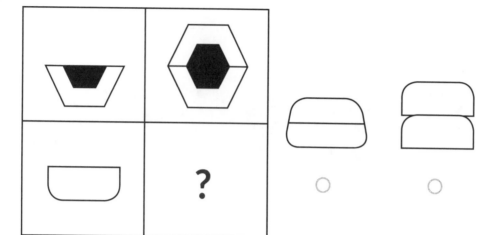

 45

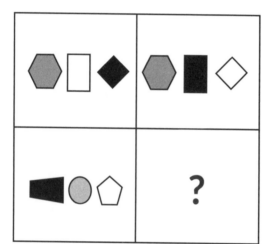

 46

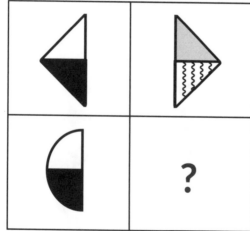

 82

47

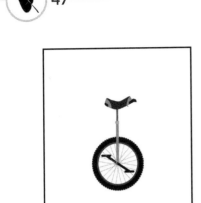

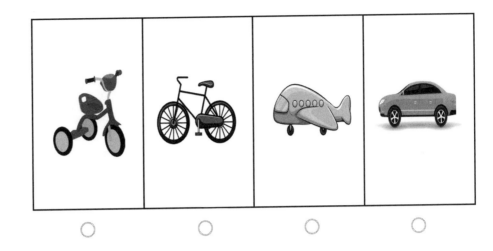

○ ○ ○ ○

 48

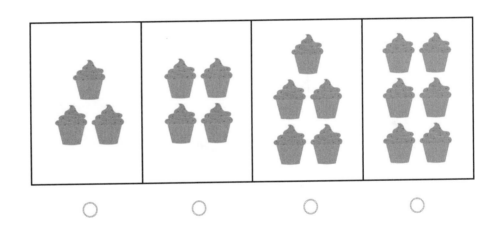

○ ○ ○ ○

49

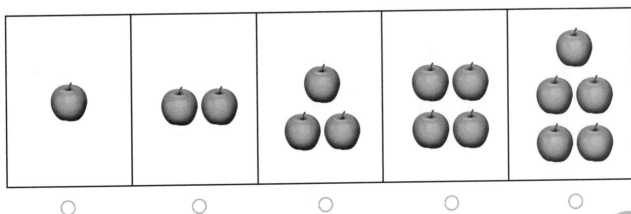

○ ○ ○ ○ ○

50

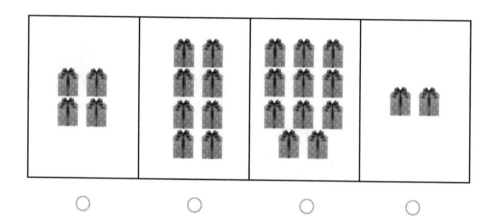

◯　　　◯　　　◯　　　◯

51

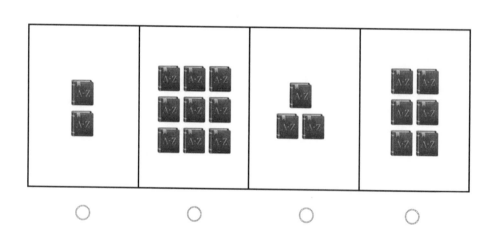

◯　　　◯　　　◯　　　◯

52

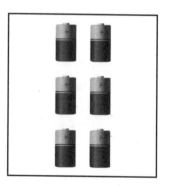
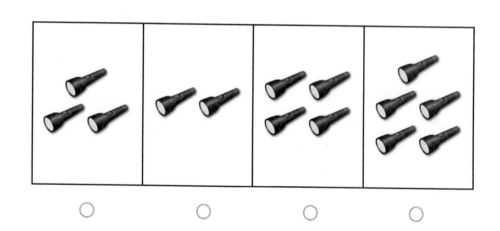

◯　　　◯　　　◯　　　◯

53

 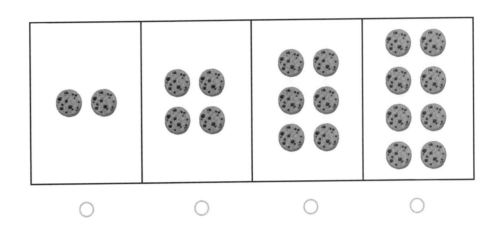

○   ○   ○   ○

 54

 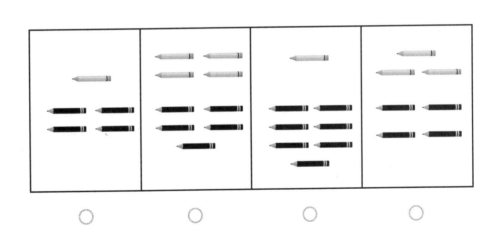

○   ○   ○   ○

Continue to the next page.

55

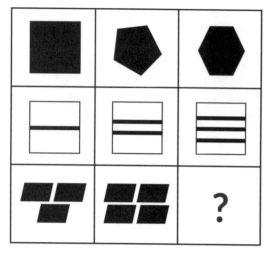

○ ○ ○ ○

 56

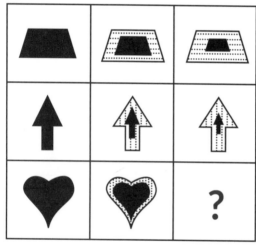

○ ○ ○ ○

 57

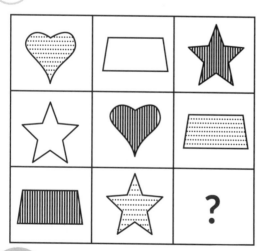

○ ○ ○ ○

End of

Practice

Question

Set

ANSWER KEY FOR WORKBOOK

Picture Classification
1. B (cuts)
2. D (animal homes)
3. D (fish)
4. E (odd numbers)
5. D (lowercase letters)
6. A (real animals)
7. B (winter clothes)
8. A (uppercase letters)
9. E (wind instruments)
10. B (half)
11. D (baby animals)
12. B (have shells)
13. C (drink containers)
14. B (community helpers / real people)
15. B (types of grain)
16. D (reptiles)
17. C (have stripes)

Figure Classification
1. B (divided in half)
2. D (rounded)
3. B (diamond in middle -OR- others have 3 different shapes;
      B only has 2, as the triangle is repeated)
4. D (shapes & small circles are opposite colors)
5. A (circle is at the same place within larger shape)
6. C (1/4 filled in)
7. E (1 diamond filled in)
8. A (4 shapes)
9. B (shapes are 1 circle, 1 star, 1 diamond)
10. D (2 dark lines, 1 gray line)
11. B (triangles)
12. C (dark circles are next to each other)
13. B (larger middle shape w/ 2 smaller versions of
      same shape on either side)
14. C (same shape, same position)
15. C (6-sided shapes)
16. D (3 shapes)
17. C (divided in half)
18. B (half of shape is dark)
19. E (3 upside-down hearts, 1 regular heart)
20. C (divided into 4 equal parts)
21. B (same 2 shapes top/bottom & left/right)
22. E (lighter line stays at the same place on the
      darker shape)

Picture Analogies
1. D
2. A (person > where person usually sleeps)
3. B (object > 1 part of object)
4. A (same kind of clothing; shirts & jackets)
5. D (objects > container)
6. C (faster action done with electrical item)
7. B (closed > open)
8. A (plant's habitat > plant)
9. C (# of vehicle wheels > vehicle)
10. D (place where you would find animal > animal)
11. A (object > where object is usually kept)
12. C (# of shape sides > # of kids)
13. A (group of same kind of object > 1 of these objects)
14. C (same kind of object; shorts & crowns)
15. B (same kind of animal; large cats & insects)
16. D (where vehicle is used > vehicle)
17. A (location > item found in location)
18. A (a stoplight has 3 lights; a pentagon has 5 sides)
19. D (a chef creates meals; a painter creates paintings)

Figure Analogies
1. D (shapes switch positions & colors)
2. B (stars become arrows; arrows become stars)
3. A (rotates clockwise, becomes white)
4. D (rotates & line is added in center)
5. D (shape in center moves to top and becomes dark)
6. C (middle shapes align horizontally; color/design
from large and small shapes switch)
7. C ("x" rotates & shapes inside reverse color)
8. B (star becomes hexagon & vice versa, they
reverse color; bottom shape reverses color)
9. A (outer shape & center shape switch)
10. D (number of dots is the same but white; shape is 3D)

Figure Analogies, continued

11. A (large shape rotates, stars align horizontally and turn white)
12. D (rotates counterclockwise, small shapes reverse color)
13. B (lines change orientation & in bottom box, separate)
14. A (top left & bottom right switch)
15. C (outer & middle shape switch positions and colors, then align vertically)
16. C (white circles become black; black become white)
17. B (1 more line is added inside the shape)
18. D (rotates clockwise)
19. A (# of sides increases by 1; 3 sides> 4 sides; 5 sides > 6 sides)
20. B (circles line up diagonally bottom left to top right, then line up vertically; on the bottom they do the opposite: circles line up horizontally, then line up diagonally top left to bottom right)

Pattern Matrices

1. D
2. C (across rows: in first box, circle(s) on left side are filled in, then in the second box the circle(s) on right side are filled in, the last box has the combination of the first two boxes filled in) (down columns, the same principle, but it occurs with the circles on the top/bottom)
3. C (diamond size alternates large & small)
4. A (each row/column has: diamond, triangle, heart)
5. C (across the rows, the second and third box show the design that was in the first box divided)
6. B (across rows shape rotates clockwise; down columns, in last column the dotted section is on left & gray section is on right)
7. A (across rows & down columns: +1 arrow)
8. C (across rows alternates down-up-down)
9. D (in rows, 1 less triangle is filled in; in columns 1 more triangle is filled in)
10. A (in rows-rotates clockwise (-90 degrees); in columns- rotates 180 degrees)
11. B (across rows, each box will have as the center shape either a square, arrow, or star; also, the number of circles around this middle shape must be the same across the row - in the last row there are 2 outer circles)

Can You Find It?

1. C   2. D   3. B   4. A   5. C   6. B   7. A   8. D   9. C   10. B   11. C   12. D   13. B   14. D
15. C   16. A   17. C   18. D   19. D   20. B   21. A   22. C

Figure Series

1. D
2. C (the triangle that's shaded rotates clockwise)
3. B (+2)
4. A (-2 filled in or +2 white)
5. D (+1 shape becomes black & in each box same shapes)
6. B (in every other box: there's the same shape type AND 1 shape is added)
7. C (heart rotates counterclockwise with the design pattern: dots, lines, gray, dots, lines)
8. A (boxes 1, 3, 5 have 4 circles; in boxes 2, 4 there is 1 circle added)
9. A (pattern: wavy line > 4 boxes with black, white, black, white > wavy line, etc.)
10. C (hexagon group rotates counterclockwise (around 45 degrees) AND hexagons switch colors)
11. D (1 arrow is added & arrows change direction)
12. B (letters are in the same order & line up vertically)

Arithmetic Reasoning

1. D   2. C   3. C   4. D   5. B   6. A   7. C   8. D   9. B   10. B   11. A   12. D

OLSAT® PRACTICE QUESTION SET: DIRECTIONS & ANSWER KEY

- Be sure to read 'Practice Question Set Instructions' first (page 64).

- This answer key is divided into charts according to OLSAT® question type so that you can easily see how your child performs in each of the test's 9 sections. Each chart includes the directions you will read to your child. It also lists the page icons and question icons that you will read to your child to assist with navigation.

1) If turning to a new page, say to your child: "Find the page where there is a(n) ___ at the bottom." (These sentences are listed in each chart in *italics*.)

2) Next, say to your child: "Find the row where there is a(n) ___. " (These are the question navigation icons listed in the first column. These are underlined.)

3) Then, read the directions to your child.

- Some question types have directions in a gray box. (For example, Picture Classification.) These question types have the same directions for all the questions of that question type.

- For the question types that do NOT have directions in a gray box (Aural Reasoning, Following Directions, and Arithmetic Reasoning), you will use the question prompts in the 'Directions' column.

OLSAT® QUESTION TYPE 1: PICTURE CLASSIFICATION

Directions for all Picture Classification questions: Look at this row of pictures. One of these pictures in the row does not belong. This picture is not like the others in the row. Which picture does not belong?

"Find the row where there is a(n) ___."	Question Number	Answer	Child's Answer
(p. 66) *"Find the page where there is a train at the bottom."* (Help child find the page where questions start.)			
Star	1	D (animal homes)	
Sun	2	E (odd numbers)	
Chair	3	C (measuring items)	

OLSAT® QUESTION TYPE 1: PICTURE CLASSIFICATION, CONTINUED

"Find the row where there is a(n) ___."	Question Number	Answer	Child's Answer
(p. 67) *"Find the page where there is a bird at the bottom."*			
Car	4	B (toys)	
Fish	5	E (sports-related)	
Fork	6	A (sports balls)	

Picture Classification Questions Answered Correctly: _____ out of 6

OLSAT® QUESTION TYPE 2: FIGURE CLASSIFICATION

Directions for all Figure Classification questions: Look at this row of pictures. One of these pictures in the row does not belong. This picture is not like the others in the row. Which picture does not belong?

"Find the row where there is a(n) ___."	Question Number	Answer	Child's Answer
(p. 68) *"Find the page where there is a house at the bottom."*			
Truck	7	D (star and heart around octagon)	
Crab	8	E (square is on the shorter straight line of the trapezoid)	
Car	9	B (3 arrow points)	
(p. 69) *"Find the page where there is a pair of glasses at the bottom."*			
Spider Web	10	C (3 shapes filled in)	

Figure Classification Questions Answered Correctly: _____ out of 4

OLSAT® QUESTION TYPE 3: AURAL REASONING

Find the row where there's (n) ___."	Question Number	Directions (Say to child)	Answer	Child's Answer
and	11	Freddie wants to see his reflection. Which object should he use to see his reflection?	D	
ish	12	In which one of these locations would a weather forecaster predict a blizzard?	A	

continued on next page

OLSAT® QUESTION TYPE 3: AURAL REASONING, CONTINUED

"Find the row where there's a(n) ___."	Question Number	Directions (Say to child)	Answer	Child's Answer
(p. 70) *"Find the page where there is an umbrella at the bottom."*				
Spiderweb	13	If your family wanted to make a budget, which of these objects would be the most helpful?	B	
Shirt	14	If you were an astronomer, which of these would you most likely use at work?	D	
Chair	15	Which one of these things would an electrician not repair?	C	
(p. 71) *"Find the page where there is a ball at the bottom."*				
Car	16	Which animal does not experience metamorphosis?	A	
Fish	17	Your friend, Lisa, and her dad went walking in the forest and got lost. They were able to find their way back using one of the items in this row. Which item would they have used?	D	
Triangle	18	Your friend, Alex, is traveling in the desert. Which one of these would he be using to travel?	A	

Aural Reasoning Questions Answered Correctly: _____ out of 8

OLSAT® QUESTION TYPE 4: FOLLOWING DIRECTIONS

"Find the row where there is a(n) __."		Directions (Say to child)	Answer	Child's Answer
(p. 72) *"Find the page where there is a table at the bottom."*				
Sun	19	Which picture shows a boy with glasses, playing with a ball next to a bike?	D	
Star	20	To complete an art project, Sophie used different art supplies. Some of these supplies are in the following pictures. She used glue, paper, colored pencils, and scissors. Which kind of supply did she not use?	B	
Shirt	21	Which picture shows 1 child facing backwards and 2 children turned to the right?	D	
(p. 73) *"Find the page where there is a hand at the bottom."*				
Web	22	Which picture shows a pair of boots with 2 gray socks and 2 white socks?	A	
Fork	23	Freddie's favorite animal has neither stripes nor spots, and it does not swim. Which one of the pictures shows Freddie's favorite animal?	C	
Bug	24	Which picture shows a letter that is neither inside the triangle nor to the left of the triangle?	B	
(p.74) *"Find the page where there is ice cream at the bottom."*				
Spoon	25	Which picture shows a number that is neither outside the circle nor to the right of the triangle?	A	
Bug	26	Which picture shows a star below a letter, a number to the right of a circle, and a letter to the right of a diamond?	D	
Chair	27	Max went to the park to look for animals. At the park, he did not see a bird, but he did see 3 squirrels and a caterpillar. Which one of the pictures shows the animals he saw?	A	
(p.75) *"Find the page where there is a leaf at the bottom."*				
Car	28	Which picture shows neither a pencil nor a crayon first, scissors in the middle, and neither a pencil nor tape last?	D	

Following Directions Questions Answered Correctly: _____ out of 10

OLSAT® QUESTION TYPE 5: FIGURE SERIES

Directions for all Figure Series questions: Look at this row of boxes. The pictures that are inside belong together in some way. Another picture should go inside the empty box. Under the boxes there is a row of pictures. Which one should go inside the empty box?

"Find the row where there is a(n) ___."	Question Number	Answer	Child's Answer
Fish	29	C (in boxes 1, 3, 5 the # of shapes increases by 1; this also happens in boxes 2, 4)	
(p. 76) *"Find the page where there is a diamond at the bottom."*			
Bird	30	C (# of spades pointing down increases by 1; spades pointing up decrease by 1)	
Crab	31	C (gray dot top left in box 1 rotates counter-clockwise in group of circles)	
(p. 77) *"Find the page where there is a bike at the bottom."*			
Spider Web	32	D (# of shapes filled with dots increases by 1)	
Pencil	33	B (gray triangles move around clockwise)	
(p. 78) *"Find the page where there is an eye at the bottom."*			
Spoon	34	C (in boxes 1, 3, 5 the # of shapes increases by 1; in boxes 2, 4 the # of shapes decreases by 1)	
Leaf	35	A (boxes 1, 3, 5 have 2 circles)	
(p. 79) *"Find the page where there is an arrow at the bottom."*			
Chair	36	D (pentagon-trapezoid-diamond-circle)	
Fork	37	C (in boxes 1, 3, 5 the # of shapes increases by 1)	

Figure Series Questions Answered Correctly: _____ out of 9

OLSAT® QUESTION TYPE 6: PICTURE ANALOGIES

Directions for all Picture Analogy questions: Look at these boxes that are on top. The pictures that are inside belong together in some way. Then, look at these boxes that are on the bottom. One of these boxes on the bottom is empty. Look next to the boxes. There is a row of pictures. Which one would go together with this picture that is in the bottom box like these pictures that are in the top boxes?

"Find the row where there is a(n) ___."	Question Number	Answer	Child's Answer
(p. 80) *"Find the page where there is a train at the bottom."*			
Leaf	38	B (opposite; happy/sad; day/night)	
Cup	39	C (faster action done with electrical item)	
Spider Web	40	D (open > closed)	
(p. 81) *"Find the page where there is a star at the bottom."*			
Bike	41	A (half > whole)	
Fish	42	B (object > where object is kept)	

Picture Analogies Questions Answered Correctly: _____ out of 5

OLSAT® QUESTION TYPE 7: FIGURE ANALOGIES

Directions for all Figure Analogy questions: Look at these boxes that are on top. The pictures that are inside belong together in some way. Then, look at these boxes that are on the bottom. One of these boxes on the bottom is empty. Look next to the boxes. There is a row of pictures. Which one would go together with this picture that is in the bottom box like these pictures that are in the top boxes?

"Find the row where there is a(n) ___."	Question Number	Answer	Child's Answer
Shirt	43	A (top 2 shapes switch position)	

(p. 82) *"Find the page where there is a fork at the bottom."*

Ant	44	C (half > whole)	
Cup	45	A (shape 2&3 switch color)	
Chair	46	C (white becomes gray; black becomes curvy lines)	

Figure Analogies Questions Answered Correctly: _____ out of 4

OLSAT® QUESTION TYPE 8: ARITHMETIC REASONING

"Find the row where there is a(n) ___."	Question Number	Directions (Say to child)	Answer	Child's Answer
		(p. 83) *"Find the page where there is a shoe at the bottom."*		
Leaf	47	There is a unicycle in the first box. Which answer choice shows something with three times the number of wheels as a unicycle?	A	
Fish	48	Sophie had the number of cupcakes in the first box. Then, her sister gives her 2 more cupcakes and her brother gives her 1 more. Which answer choice shows how many she has now?	C	
Shirt	49	Freddie and Max each picked one apple from a tree. Sophie picked 2 apples. Which answer choice shows how many apples the kids picked all together?	D	
		(p. 84) *"Find the page where there is a black rectangle at the bottom."*		
Spider Web	50	May has the bags that you see in the first box. She puts 3 presents in the white bag. She puts 4 presents in each one of the black bags. Which answer choice shows the total number of presents she put in the bags?	C	
Fork	51	A group of 3 friends must each read at least 3 books a day. Which answer choice shows the possible number of books that the group reads all together in a day?	B	
Spoon	52	Alex bought the number of batteries in the first box. He will put 2 batteries in each flashlight that is empty. How many flashlights will now work?	A	

"Find the row where there is a(n) ___."	Question Number	Directions (Say to child)	Answer	Child's Answer
		p. 85) *"Find the page where there is a fish at the bottom."*		
Bike	53	In the first box are the number of carrots Sophie has eaten. For each carrot she eats, she gets to eat 2 cookies. Which answer choice shows the number of cookies she gets to eat?	C	
Shirt	54	In the first box are Max's pencils. He has 2 gray pencils and 3 black pencils. Anya has half as many gray pencils as Max. She also has 4 more black pencils than Max. Which one of the answer choices shows how many pencils Anya has?	C	

Arithmetic Reasoning Questions Answered Correctly: _____ out of 8

OLSAT® QUESTION TYPE 9: PATTERN MATRIX

Directions for all Pattern Matrix questions: Look at these pictures that are inside the boxes. Look at the last box. It is empty. Beside the boxes there is a row of pictures. Which one should go inside the empty box that is in the bottom row?

"Find the row where there is a(n)___."	Question Number	Answer	Child's Answer
		(p. 86) *"Find the page where there is a car at the bottom."*	
Ant	55	C (shape sides/# of lines/# of shapes increases by 1 across the rows)	
Cup	56	C (3rd box in the row has same design as 2nd box, but smaller middle shape)	
Chair	57	D (each row/column has: heart, star, trapezoid and one shape each with dots, vertical lines, white)	

Pattern Matrix Questions Answered Correctly: _____ out of 3

Check out our OLSAT® Grade 1 & OLSAT® K/Pre-K books!

Plus, visit **www.GatewayGifted.com**

today for a FREE eBook of 40+ questions.

Did your child finish the exercises?
Here's a certificate for your new detective! (Please cut along the dotted lines.)

The Kids' Detective Agency

Congratulations to:

_____

Our Newest Member!